W9-ASK-998

The oilmen

This book, telling the story of men
and women at work in a great industry,
was made possible by the cooperation
of the employees of Shell Oil Company.

Text by **CHARLES PARKER**

Design by **FREDERICK H. ROBERTS**

Copyright 1952 by **RINEHART & COMPANY, INC.**

The Oilmen

A Photographic Story
by Thomas Hollyman

Rinehart & Company, Inc.

New York   Toronto

Their energy moves a nation

These people do ten jobs. One studies million-year-old fossils. A second drills wells three miles deep. A third splits molecules. Others load barges, type letters, or deliver gasoline. These oilmen, introducing the main sections of this book, are typical of the thousands who work for a single company — and of the two million who work in the industry as a whole. Few of these people ever meet, yet their efforts, properly linked, provide the nation with more than half its energy and give it the greatest freedom of movement in the history of mankind.

THIS GEOLOGIST searches for oil from an office, where he and other scientists run a central intelligence agency. They sift and combine clues sent in by dozens of field geologists. And they take nothing for granted. They scrutinize aerial photos for promising sites and study descriptions, made with the help of miniature earthquakes, of formations far underground. They take a census of tiny fossils and analyze rocks, like the one the geologist holds. Then they mark their findings on a big map that traces the paths of detective scientists looking for signs of oil in mountains, deserts, even under the ocean floor.

Field geologists

Commuting by helicopter to out-of-the-way spots balances time they spend playing mountain goat.

A chip off an old rock, spotted on an aerial photograph, is a red hot clue in a geologist's whodunit.

study the surface for clues to what's underneath

Seen through their sights, a sloping bed of sandstone can become a key to great buried treasures.

If he finds a lead in the field (*right*) he sends it to the office, where it's added to the data on a big map.

If clues are good surveyors run long straight lines

They map a rough-floored California valley as carefully as a city lot. Oil-hunting is costly and sloppy work can mean ruin.

Seismologists seeking other clues follow the surveyed line with a miniature drilling rig and sink tiny wells at regular intervals—but not for oil.

Next, they hook cables to cylindrical shock detectors that oilmen call "jugs." When everything is set they stuff the shallow wells with dynamite.

so seismic crews can make deep-level tests—with

Firing a charge, whose dust blows out an "L" shaped pipe, seismic crews start a pint-size earthquake. Its shock waves flash far underground.

Formations that might hold oil betray themselves by reflecting shock waves. These are caught by jugs and recorded as wiggly lines (right).

dynamite

Hovering mosquito-like over a Louisiana marsh, they prepare new seismic studies.

They reel out cables that carry the tell-tale shock waves from sensitive receiving jugs.

And they plant the jugs as they go, in holes poked into the muck with a stick.

Linking jug and cable in a few seconds, they buzz along to plant and link some more.

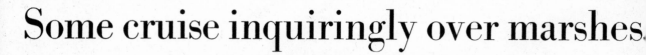

Queerest job of all is that of the man in the boat towed behind the marsh buggy. He plants and fires charges.

They reel him in for lunch. The hollow-wheeled monster beats the mud. Canopies cut sun. Nothing stops insects.

Some cruise inquiringly over marshes.

On a recording boat, 10 miles offshore, these sea-going seismologists reel out jugs, cables.

At the same time, on the shooting boat, other oilmen are beginning to "plant" the dynamite.

And the blast sends them a story of what's under the Gulf, told in wiggles on a long tape.

Moving at a good clip in converted crash boats, marine seismic crews can survey 50 miles of ocean floor a day.

They must know what they're doing and exactly where they do it. Shoran, a type of radar, pin points every shot.

while others blast for signs in the Gulf of Mexico

Every blast their field crews fire echoes in this office, where experts interpret seismic records in order to select and combine good clues.

Many oilmen are women. She's a geological draftsman, putting strategically important data on a map to be used in planning a campaign.

These sift all the clues, make the big decision

The district geologist is another of the canny hunters who help decide if and how the search will go on.

These geologists at the division level also take their crack at the field crews' evidence and add their judgment to the plan.

The final word comes from the high command of exploration. Their okay starts the drill that hunts for oil.

He can help the search with fresh evidence a million years old, tiny fossils skilfully sifted from rocks the field men find. Identifying and counting any of 30,000 "bugs", he spots formations that might hold oil

THE LAND MAN goes to work when the oil hunters say the clues look good enough. He leases the land where the clues were found. Fast-working and alert in competing with other companies, he's also a good mixer, talking easily with land owners about weather, kids, cattle and the oil that may lie beneath their fields. When a bargain is struck, he gives the owner a check and agrees to begin drilling by a certain date or give the lease back. Meanwhile the owner uses his land as before and receives rentals from the oil company. If oil is found, he gets still more, in royalties. To many a farmer, the land man is the oil company. And no wonder. A visit from him can change a man's whole life.

Part sleuth and part diplomat, this oilman gets land

VENDEE INDEX
PARISH OF
EAST BATON ROUGE
LA.

C

Then he visits the owner. In this instance it is a farmer near Baton Rouge. The conversation begins informally but soon gets around to the chief business at hand.

Before he can lease the first square foot of land for drilling, the land man searches old records to find out who owns it.

to drill on

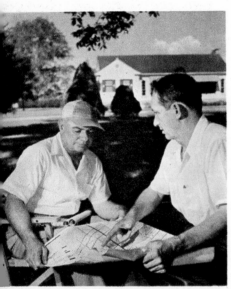

He explains the company plans, shows the farmer where wells will be drilled.

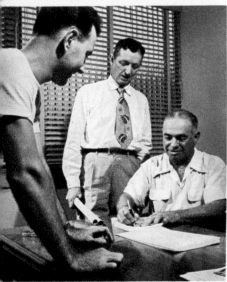

Then he serves as lawyer. The farmer signs lease and a third man witnesses.

The land man stays in touch with the farmer, even after the lease is signed and the company has started drilling.

This farmer was lucky. The new well came in—oilman's term meaning struck oil—and now he's getting his royalties.

And these write a biography of every well that's

Scouts, working for various companies, meet at Midland, Texas, to trade information about new wells being drilled in their territories. They also get rock samples from wells *(right)* for analysis. The scouts' records are giving oilmen wider knowledge of things underground.

drilled

WHEN THE DRILLING CREW moves in the chips are down. For these are the men who get the oil, if it's there, or spend as much as $1,000,000 before finding it's not.

They move with the split-second timing of a professional backfield in one of the fastest, toughest, most exciting jobs anywhere. The machine they use looks like a giant windmill with the blades removed. Actually, it's a 15-story-high derrick, supporting a long steel pipe with a drilling bit at the bottom. When they are not babying the bit into the hole, they're snaking pipe out to change bits, uncoupling in a matter of hours enough plumbing for a respectable skyscraper. They drill wherever the geologist's clues and the land man's leases take them. And the oldest never outgrow the excitement of the last few hours of drilling before the big question is answered: is it another well—or a dry hole?

Their drill can reach oil

And this grimy artist, handling the big machine with surprising delicacy, lowers the bit to begin drilling. He's the driller. There's only one such oilman to a crew, and he's the boss.

Respectfully known as a roughneck on the drilling crew, this oilman guides gear-like drilling bit into the hole.

even three miles down

Strictly speaking, oilmen cannot be said to have a well until oil appears. Hence this driller is "making hole". He tells by the feel of his rig how things are going 15,000 feet below.

Oilmen's tools are so heavy they need other tools to handle them. This tackle helps pull drill stem from hole. ▶

He can drill a curved hole three miles into the earth and reach any desired objective.

This oilman has knocked off for lunch a few feet from the steadily turning drill stem.

Men on a drilling crew may be veterans of scores of wells or college football players on summer vacation jobs.

The best are tough, earthy, independent as hogs on ice but capable of teamwork found in few other industries.

And he considers a $175 bit that wore to nubbins making 7 feet of hole in 11 hours.

These roughnecks uncouple joints, or sections, of drill stem three at a time, as the driller raises the stem from the hole.

A "round trip" — pulling stem from hole, changing bit and putting it back — takes the precision of a string quartet.

They "play" a giant rig with musician's skill

Derrick man wears a safety harness as he manhandles pipe from a monkey board 125 feet up *(right)*. Called the rig's best job, it offers good view and nice breeze.

The 5-ton traveling block, lifting pipe from the hole, shoots by like a boxcar.

and take turns as cowboys high above the ground

s the block goes by and stops, he snares pipe, pulls it over to pipe rack. He reverses
s job when it's time to run the drill stem back down the hole and resume drilling.

Good men in tall derricks are the answer to an oilman's prayer. Handling the
heavy 40-foot "joints" of pipe three at a time, they help speed costly drilling job.

They set up drilling rigs at sea if the signs are

At home with either sea gulls or sage brush, oil-men flood and sink barges for use as drilling platforms in the Gulf of Mexico or mount a rig on an LST and cruise to the newest drilling site.

Drilling at sea means living with the job and living well. The crew is eating aboard the con-verted LST, somewhere off the Louisiana coast.

good, but the odds against finding oil don't change

He's a member of a crew that missed. They drilled in the Gulf for weeks and ran many drill stem tests. This final check on the last test proved that the well was a dry hole.

Oilmen tackling this California field slice mountains, bulldoze roads and haul in rigs for new wells. ▶

Finding oil means more work: developing a field

The job may involve thousands of men and last for years. Eventually, oil stops flowing of its own and must be pumped.

THERE'S A SPECIAL GROUP of oilmen who channel crude oil from wells into pipe lines that feed the refineries. One of these men, shown on the opposite page, keeps tabs on wells, using many-branched arrangements of pipes and valves to regulate the flow of oil to storage tanks. These serve as local collection points. And here, the pipe liners take over, men who build and run a continent-spanning network of underground highways. Their transportation system carries a liquid cargo that is seldom seen but never stops moving. Through their big lines, the oilmen move petroleum over mountains, under rivers and fields to the greatest collection points of all — the refinery tank farms.

Once captured, oil never rests. These men measure it, clean it and pass it on

When the production men have done their work, the gauger's job starts. He measures oil flowing into tanks from wells in a West Texas field.

Wherever there are oil fields, there are tanks like these, serving as collection points. From here, oil goes to bigger gathering places.

...a-going gaugers check the oil from five ...ells from the platform in the Gulf. And ...e lone pumper examines a flow-control-...g Christmas tree on a California well.

Some oilmen run trap farms catching and separating everything that comes from wells—crude oil, water and gas.

The crude oil emerging from the trap farms moves on to the refineries. The gas goes on to natural gasoline plants.

Pipe liners lay a line big enough to crawl through across a thousand miles of country in a few months.

When they've laid it they level the ground, replace fences, leave things as they were in the beginning.

Pipe liners lace the nation with big steel tubes

Starting rough, with ditchers and bulldozers, they end gently, coating and wrapping the pipe to protect steel.

They examine the coating with an electric detector to avoid flaws that would admit water and start corrosion.

inking distant fields with main refining centers

Some operate the lines, plan new ones, or fly patrol

This crude oil pipe line dispatcher does an oilman's job in a highly specialized communications center.

He funnels crude oil from the Ventura and coastal fields through lines to refineries near Los Angeles.

Other oilmen, far from ditchers and wrapping machines, lay more pipes on paper for tomorrow's o

o spot leaks

hese pipe liners plan new large-diameter lines to move ude oil from Oklahoma to refineries in the Midwest.

The oilman on the ground runs a pump station that pushes oil toward refineries. Here, he gets the "all's well" sign from the flying oilman who looks for signs of leaks.

From his normal altitude, about 150 feet, he easily sees stains of escaping oil, gullies washed around the pipe, or anything else unusual that might check the flow of crude.

The gauger measures tides o

The vigil over crude oil never stops, even at the refinery tank farm, such as this one in Californ
Here, lonely gaugers, living in a world of shapes and shadows, keep a running inventory on an oce
of oil rolling into great storage tanks from wells in oil fields that may be hundreds of miles awa

oil, sees only cupfuls

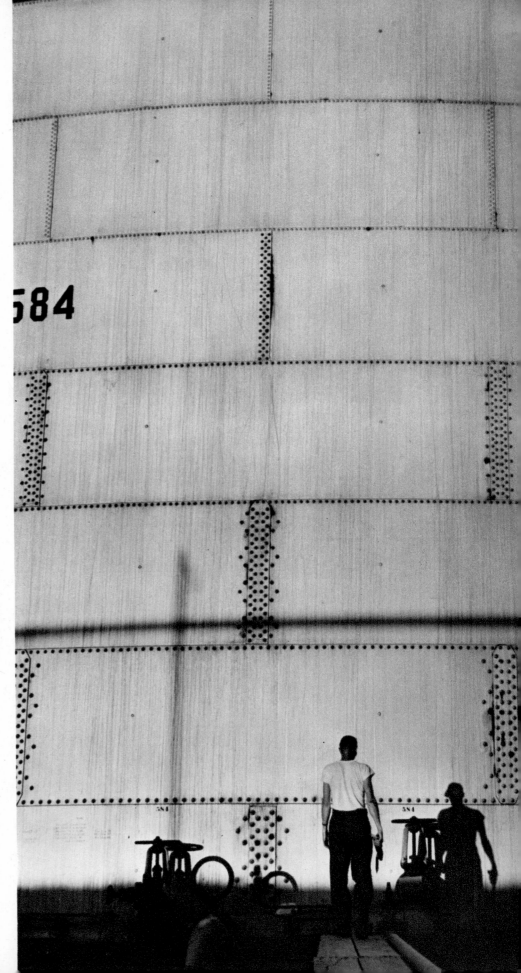

THE REFINER'S SKILL has kept the oil industry from becoming a ten show. It nearly started as one. For years, petroleum was best known as a cure all peddled by banjo-strumming medicine men. Then the refiner showed how it could be distilled to make lamp oil.

Ever since, he has been multiplying his products. Now there are more than a thousand and the list is still growing. It begins with lighter fluid and spot remover, runs through gasoline, jet fuel, kerosene, fuel oils, lubricants scores of chemicals, and ends with such solid stuff as asphalt and coke

To make these, he has improved his plant with some of the bigges machines ever built. One, the cat cracker on the opposite page, is 14 storie high and has its own elevator. In this and other units, with their jungles o connecting pipe, he cooks, cracks, chills and squeezes crude oil into thing men use—by the billions of gallons a year.

In a steel city they keep endless watch on a steady

pulse of oil

Their view changes from day to night, but not their job. They split the incoming stream of crude into a thousand different products.

Thirty-five hundred oilmen, working in shifts around the clock, run this refinery in Illinois. Men and women of varied crafts and skills keep oil moving steadily through the plant to meet a demand that increases every year.

He's making toluene for high explosives and aviation gasoline. Like most refiners, he never sees the stuff he's working with. But from his desk in the control room of the toluene unit, he can check the instruments guiding the machines that do the job.

Another of the refiner's skills is that of inspector. They check parts for towers that separate boiling chemicals.

Some oilmen help run a refinery. Many others, like this welder, help keep it running, shutting down units periodically and putting them back into top condition.

He's a milk man in reverse, delivering empties to refinery units, taking full ones to the laboratory technicians who test all the products for quality.

Refiners are welders, "milk men," boilermakers

Here's the boilermaker, chipping the inside of a b reactor vessel during a routine maintenance jo

They live — wide awake — in a plumber's nightmare

efiners give strange names to the jobs that must be done in moving oil through the ght pipes in the right direction. These clear-eyed oilmen are called "blind" changers.

Engineers planned this maze so systematically that refiners can easily trace any pipe they want. This set serves a unit that distills products out of crude oil.

e moves with easy confidence among miles of pipe—some inter-
ced, others parallel, like these carrying products to a pump station.

and know jus
and towe
long—where i

They're on old familiar ground, high in a caged-in safety ladder on a column that produces solvents.

And they know, as well as the back of their hand, the shapes of the tanks holding finished products.

what each tube holds—how should go next

Five floors up in a cat cracker they work in abstract pattern toward a real end: more gasoline.

They shut down units for overhaul on regular schedule. The crane men hoist the big, heavy parts.

THIS INTENT YOUNG MAN is a researcher. For each scientist like him in his company, there are 16 other oilmen, from the salesman on the road to the boss in head office. They rely on him for new processes and products, and so does every one else who uses anything made from oil. He's well equipped for the job. He has at least one degree in science, probably two or three. He uses an electron microscope as easily as most people use a cigarette lighter. But his best tool is the huge backlog of knowledge built up by other scientists. Drawing on this fund, he and his associates may try for years to reach a highly-prized goal. In the long run, their doggedness and skill pay off in new knowledge, better fuels and lubricants, or brand new products made from oil.

Paid simply to think, this oilman tackles jobs whose names most people cannot even pronounce. He does his thinking in Houston, Texas.

A scientist on the staff of an oil exploration laboratory, he is shown here thrashing out a knotty problem in interpretation of seismic data.

Ideas: he sweats them out and others try them out

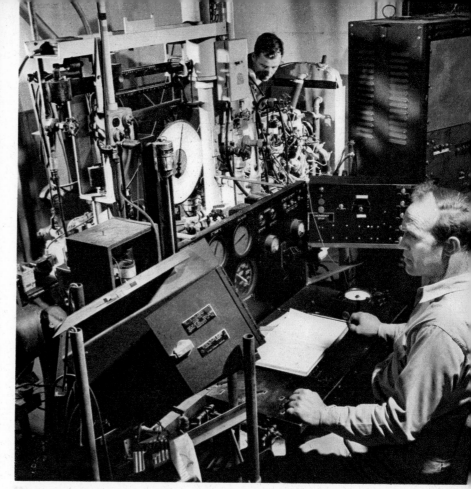

Stresses this man puts on materials in a California laboratory may lead to knowledge that helps other oilmen do better jobs at a refinery in Illinois.

In the same laboratory, another scientist "drives" thousands of miles a year with a unit that simulates all kinds of traffic conditions for tests of gasolines and engines.

He compounds synthetic rubber from petroleum in a little test mill. Ideas that work out here may be put to more elaborate tests.

Whether he's improving a product or a process or adding to the total knowledge of scientific principles, he does an oilman's job.

All year long the laboratory scientists at a big Illinois refinery study various types of fuels and engines. One day, each spring, they have a picnic.

The main event is the Wood River Mileage Marathon, an auto "race" held to see who can get the most miles from one gallon of gasoline.

And some take good ideas on an oilman's holiday

asting with motor off is main key to high mileage. over-inflated tires, filed tread, balanced wheels.

Another technique is setting carburetor for perfect air-fuel mixture. Girls over-adjusted and lost out.

Tuning the motor is important, but economical gun-and-roll driving technique wins the Marathon.

ontestants all use family-type cars, and many of them d streamlined shells to reduce the wind resistance.

Kids love the Marathon and wives accept it gracefully. Hard-racing scientists *(left)* control their speed so as to average less than 15 miles an hour but have scored as high as 149 miles to a gallon.

When these oil scientists needed a special column for analytical work, a glass-blowing oilman made it

An age-old craft is both his work and his hobby

This glass blower in a California laboratory fashions miniature, transparent refinery units.

Research scientists striking out into new problems may need apparatus that is not on the laboratory shelf. The glass blower turns it out from scratch, using this fire lathe to change the shape of plain glass cylinders.

He also doodles rather well. Besides saucy birds he makes unlikely beasts and dainty ballerinas.

THIS OILMAN-FARMER has an improbable job. He grows weak crop
and strong bugs on purpose. He also grows grade A weeds. At the sam
time, however, he raises top-notch produce and helps develop new chem
icals to kill bugs and control weeds. The net profit from his work i
knowledge. He's ranch foreman on an experimental farm, one of man
oilmen who stand with one foot in science and one in industry, passin
knowledge back and forth between the two. Thanks to their strategi
position, these men have been able to turn up fertilizers that lead t
enormous boosts in food production, hormone sprays that control th
time of harvest, almost to the day, solutions that kill weeds without hurt
ing crops. Drawing oilmen's paychecks, they never go near an oil fiel
or refinery and stop at service stations only as customers. They spen
their days making oil work for a world plagued by a ravenous appetite

The plant pathologist looks for signs of disease in seedlings at a big farm-laboratory in California

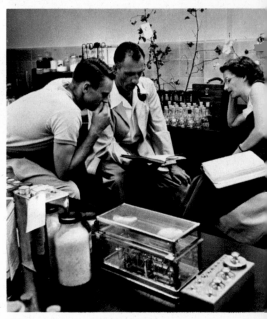

They review a test of an oil product used to make cotton leaves fall earlier and so make picking easy.

They look like

These green-thumbed oilmen let their crops grow just long enough, then harvest them for science.

Ideas the oilmen hatch out on their laboratory farm quickly scatter to commercial farms all over the country, give bigger, better crops.

They have developed new sprays, like this for grapes, and new fertilizers, then designed equipment for applying them most effectively.

farmers, think like scientists and work like both

The agricultural agent is an independent operator. He gets ammonia from other oilmen who make it, then sells it to farmers as fertilizer.

Near Lodi, in the California wine country, he visits big growers and tells them how ammonia made by oilmen can be used as gas to help crops.

Some oilmen fatten land on petrochemicals

Or he can show how it works on a nearby farm. The ammonia is simply injected into the earth through little tubes set behind the cultivator blades.

An easy-going character, saturated with agricultural lore, he can talk well about crops or chemical to farmers who grow anything from Asparagus to Zucchini.

And he shows, in a big irrigated field of sugar beets, how crops are improved when the right chemical made by oilmen is shot back into the earth.

The ammonia he trucks out in steel cylinders is rich in nitrogen, vital food for plants. Piped into irrigation water, it seeps through soil to crops.

THIS OILMAN, who loads barges in Los Angeles, is one of a colorful crew of movers. Another is a tanker captain who reads Dickens on the run from New Orleans to New York. A third drives a truck in Minneapolis. These men are specialists, picking up products in one place and laying them down 50 or 2000 miles away. For refineries where products are made are not necessarily near places where products are used. There may be a wide gap between refinery tanks that first receive gasoline and fuel oil and the cars and homes that use them. The movers cross this gap through countless channels, on land, underground and over water. They're experts. They can move two gallons of oil 2000 miles for less than it costs to mail a postal card.

Some sample tanker cargoes *(left)*, and others check barge loads bound up the Mississippi from Louisiana.

At a refinery near Los Angeles these oilmen load sea-going tankers with gasoline for Portland and Seattle.

They pick

nd on a pier in New Jersey he unloads the *Cherry Valley*, out of New -leans with an assortment of products oilmen call a "drug store" cargo.

These movers disperse products into streams that keep branching and moving faster. He swings loading arm into place and fills a 10,000 gallon tank car in 20 minutes.

products at refineries and start the big deliveries

These direct a swift, silent, unseen movement

The operator of this products pipe line pump station in Illinois has a nice house and just strolls across lawn to work.

In New York, 600 miles away, they channel 22 products through the line, tracing the movement with a control board.

His pump moves oil from the refinery toward a big layover point. A teletype from New York tells what product is due next.

The various batches of products flow through the line one right after another with no separation between batches, yet no mixing.

And this oilman is climbing up to gauge a product that others have moved into the tank. The scene is a terminal, or distribution center.

The oilmen have built such terminals across the nation to receive and store big volumes of products as backlogs to insure local supplies.

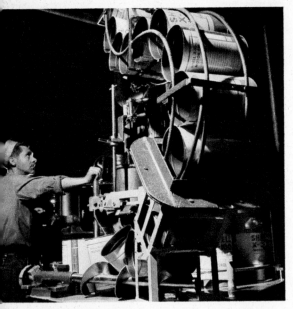

He modifies the flow of product, puts big bulk into small containers for easy use.

And he feeds other products into steel drums, controlling the quantity he puts in with an automatic scale.

When products are packed, he passes them on to the railroaders and truckers for their next long ride.

while others blend, package and deliver the goods

At a big compounding plant in New Jersey, he watches more oil than most oilmen ever see. And he sees a wide range of products.

Through such great distribution centers pass lubricants, fuels, asphalt, solvents, anti-freeze and a score of chemicals *(right)*.

THERE'S NO TIN HAT in her wardrobe, no laboratory coat in his hall closet. Neither the girl nor the man she's helping has any of the badges that mark the oilmen on the preceding pages. Still, these two are important oilmen, members of big clerical and technical staffs.

From salesmen, movers, refiners and drillers, they gather facts the planners need in coordinating their company's far-flung yet closely-related operations. With the right facts, the planners can decide how many wells should be drilled, what pipe lines laid, which refineries expanded and how all this is to be paid for. The top planners sit at the very center of the organization, shaping policies that keep the whole show going. It's a key spot. They handle it smoothly because they know all the jobs from finding crude oil to selling gasoline and how each job meshes with the rest.

Salesmen set the pace for the other oilmen. They

In a marketing office, they sort the orders that keep other oilmen busy.

In the field, a salesman serves as a consulting engineer. This one knows railroading.

determine the demand and relay the call for action

His chart helps pick the oil to keep the machines of industry going smoothly.

Notes on this man's pad move high octane gasoline and lubricants to planes.

Time for decision. The vice president in charge of production presents a new drilling program to the president and other vice presidents. Their policies must be sound if the company is to provide its share of the nation's oil and hold its own in a ruggedly competitive industry.

Top planners have top responsibility; they plan

Refinery executives develop the top planners' broad policies into specific projects. And many other oilmen translate policy into action from oil field to service station.

and coordinate their company's operation

THE MAN who runs the service station is the one oilman everybody knows. And here, helping his wife clean his station window, is a good example, Scotty McKechnie, West Haven, Connecticut.

Scotty had had a service station in West Haven for several years. He'd been running his own show—wasn't on any one else's payroll—and he'd done pretty well. But he thought he could do even better if he made some changes. That meant putting out all his own cash, and borrowing more, to get better equipment. It was too big a step to take without advice. So one day Scotty talked his idea over with some of the oilmen from the company that sells him his gasoline. They'd worked with stations all over the country and could tell him from their experience how best to carry out his plans.

Like many another oilman's project, Scotty's plan for a new service station took shape during a midnight chat over coffee in his kitchen.

His guest, an experienced representative of the company that supplies his gasoline, told Scotty his plan was sure to bring him more business.

Scotty's ideas were soon translated into action

...e got expert help from retail men who analyzed ...s old set-up and offered plans for a better one.

...e company real estate man ironed out zoning ...blems: what he could build, where and how.

Scotty's plan began to crystallize at a meeting in Boston with some of the company's sales executives. Engineers, using scale models, helped him design the new building, locate gasoline pumps and place the flood lights.

...help went beyond planning. Architects and ...neers helped Scotty check all construction.

A traffic count showing which way most traffic passed his place enabled Scotty to spot his pumps.

Drivers like to see a station well ahead. Scotty learned to place sign so his could be seen easily.

A truck driver from the New Haven terminal filled Scotty's new tanks with their first load of gasoline—made in Texas and shipped to the east coast by tanker.

Meanwhile a merchandising expert had arranged the shelves in Scotty's show room so people could see the stock easily, perhaps remember things their cars needed.

By the morning of opening day, Scotty and the company men had the station completely fitted out and ready for a booming trade.

They didn't wait long for customers to come in. Business started briskly soon after the station opened and got better as the day went on.

By the end of the day, Scotty's friendly grin had become a perma-nent fixture. He had good reason to be confident about the future.

For 30,000 other oilmen, from the planners in head office to the drill-ers in the oil fields, were backing him up with all their experience.

With other oilmen's help, he made the idea work

And at the other end of Scotty's hose, 2,000 miles away, this oilman starts the cycle again